THE
RUDE
DICTIONARY

THE

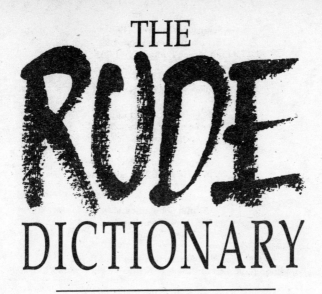

RUDE

DICTIONARY

A dictionary of words that
adults never tell you!

Compiled by Jim Howes
Illustrated by Terry Denton

Hippo

Scholastic Children's Books,
Scholastic Publications Ltd,
7-9 Pratt Street, London NW1 0AE, UK

Scholastic Inc.,
555 Broadway, New York, NY 10012, USA

Scholastic Canada Ltd,
123 Newkirk Road, Richmond Hill,
Ontario, Canada L4C 3G5

Ashton Scholastic Pty Ltd,
PO Box 579, Gosford, New South Wales,
Australia

Ashton Scholastic Ltd,
Private Bag 92801, Penrose, Auckland,
New Zealand

First published in Australia by Omnibus Books, 1992
This edition published in Britain by Scholastic Publications Ltd, 1994

Text copyright © Jim Howes, 1992
Illustrations copyright © Terry Denton, 1992
Cover illustration copyright © Rowan Barnes-Murphy, 1994

ISBN: 0 590 55614 2

Printed by Cox & Wyman Ltd, Reading, Berks

Foreword

Everybody loves being rude, at least a bit, at least sometimes, especially when you can get away with it. Like being *asked* to spit in the dentist's chair (well, in the funny sink, that is—dentists don't really like you to spit in their chairs). It always took me an extra swig or two of the glass and a good swill to work up a respectable glob ... and it was all allowed! Then there's the burp that's compulsory after dinner when your host comes from one of those Middle Eastern countries where they wait for the guest's mega-burp to show how much they have enjoyed the meal. Imagine actually being *expected* to burp. What a gas!

Trouble is, there are not many ways left where we are allowed to be rude. We've all become so polite that we are in danger of evolving into a species that will be too embarrassed to breathe out in public without first using a mouthwash.

But it doesn't have to happen. Once you have read this book, you will have a chance to free the world of its overkill on politeness. This is your key to a rude world, but—and here's the kicker—you won't get into any trouble for using the words in here. They are all real words which have been lost over the centuries, under the cruel rule of the POs (Polite Ones). Now is your chance to spread the word, to free civilisation from the chains of politeness. Rude people of the world, unite! Go out and be rude!

Aa

affle—the small cloud of steam above a fresh doggy-doo.

aggling—the annoying way some people show off how well they can gargle by singing at the same time.

ammlit—the little thing that floats on top of a drink and which always stays just where you want to drink from, no matter how carefully or quickly you try to get it on the other side by turning the glass round.

anti-jumjum—any piece of clothing, such as a T-shirt, worn in a special way so as to hide an embarrassing stain. It can also be a peculiar way of standing or walking used to hide the stain. See **jumjum**.

arm-restling—the quiet, undeclared war between people in a movie theatre who both want to use the arm-rest between their seats. Believed to be the origin of the sport of arm-*w*restling.

awespray—the pattern created by an unchecked sneeze. Visible for a short time in midair, or for longer on the empty dinner plate next to you.

ayrkarver—someone who cannot explain anything without drawing every word in the air. If they had to keep their hands in their pockets, they would be speechless.

Bb

bawlter—any ball that hits a player in a place which hurts greatly but is too rude for them to name or clutch in their agony.

belay-beloo—the dance done by anyone who, instead of hitting the nail, has just hit their finger with the hammer, and who can't swear because their grandparents are in the same room.

binky—when two pages of a new book are stuck together. When you try to separate them, you tear one from the spine so that you end up with one long, floppy page.

biskefts—the small bits of dry stuff that gather in the corners of the eyes overnight.

blanker—the look of innocence put on by the guilty when they are accused.

blimper—a pimple that never fully develops.

bloster—the mark left when someone wearing too much lipstick kisses you.

bloth—a colour or, more often, the loss of colour. Used to describe the vegetables served in school canteens and in the cafeterias of large stores, where the orange carrots, green peas and yellow pumpkin have all been cooked until they reach the same pasty, pale yellowish tone of bloth.

blundagrundge—a pretend swear word, used by people who need to swear but who would be in trouble if they did, e.g. the Prince of Wales or the Archbishop of Canterbury or other people who have to pretend to be polite in public, including the school principal who has just stumbled into the corner of the table during school assembly.

bognee—the frozen smile of someone who has just made a loud, rude bottom "burp" which everyone around them heard, and there isn't a dog in the room they can blame for it.

bom-boms—the hard, white, lumpy bits in salami and black pudding.

boomsha—being caught in an embarrassing position, e.g. you are getting changed in the jeans shop when the curtain is pulled back and it's Tiffany Ronubbler from school with three of her friends and they've all got polaroid cameras, or when everybody on the school bus sees your grandma kiss you and carry your bag when you get off.

bootum—a very droopy bottom.

brawnbees—what looks like female breasts on a fat male person.

brindle—any part of clothing (usually underwear) that rides up uncomfortably into the crack of the bottom where it gets stuck. See **debrindling**.

brooth—the cloud made on glass by breathing on it with the mouth wide open. This is sometimes used by secret agents as a way of leaving messages. The agent marks the glass with a finger. When another agent breathes on it, the brooth reveals a message. The glass surfaces used most often for this were the windows of public phone boxes, hence the term "phone brooth".

buffcote—the shine on a bald man's head. Sometimes the polished look on a sweaty nose.

bukkley—the way your legs look bent when you're standing in shallow water.

Cc

cawgrimp—the cruel grin teachers can't help
giving when they know they've caught a student
they hate in the act of doing something wrong.

chibbling—the dangerous art of nose-picking by teenagers who wear gold rings through their noses.

chubkin—the lump you feel in your throat when you are upset.

clunkrubble—anything found at the bottom of the saucepan, mug or bowl at the end of a meal and which was not supposed to be there, e.g. a spider that was resting in a mug before cocoa was poured in, or the sock that was lost two days ago but has just reappeared at the bottom of the muesli bin.

The most famous clunkrubble was a near-full roll of toilet paper which, in the dark of the evening camp ground, was left in the pot while all the other ingredients for stew were added. Although the dish seemed to need more water, campers enjoyed the extra fibre.

crawdle—the way someone walks when they have something unpleasant (e.g. a skug) stuck to the sole of their shoe. See **skug**.

creet—the stuff you can scrape off your teeth and wipe on the towels and tell your parents you have really cleaned your teeth.

crink-crunk—the small crack of the bottom that can still be seen above droopy shorts.

crobbige—the ancient art of not using a hand-kerchief.

crukk—the brittle skin that forms on the outside of a cowpat which is still soft and squidgy on the inside. A crukk is usually just hard enough to trick someone (e.g. a cowpat thrower-in-training) into thinking that the pat is hard enough to pick up.

crumfrag—the smell of a classroom on a wet day, often straight after break time.

cubleff—the feeling that comes from putting on warm socks or pyjamas that have just come out of the drier.

currintz—the dead, black stuff stuck to the fly swat.

Dd

dapdig—a man who wears his shirt unbuttoned to the navel, has a wig on his chest and wears a long, artificial gold chain around his neck.

debrindling—the pulling of one's pants with the thumb and forefinger to remove a brindle without being seen. See **brindle**.

depwagg—the floppy space in the seat of a pair of baggy trousers.

dippok—those places that you want to go to which are always in the fold of the map you are using.

ditwimblies—that part of the nose wipe that was not a success.

doohovers—the vapours from a marathon runner's freshly removed sneakers.

dopp—the sound made when a bird passes wind.

dozze—a nose pressed up against the window.

dozze-print—the sloppy mark left behind when a nose has been pressed up against the window.

driggments—the patterns made on a black T-shirt by heaps of dandruff.

dropping a humple—saying something embarrassing. In olden days, a humple was a small cloth worn as underwear. Going to the toilet, or getting changed, meant having to remove or "drop" one's humple. Being caught without one's humple was very embarrassing.

dubber—the last bit of toilet paper that is mostly stuck to the roll and is too small to use anyway.

dunfundling—putting your fingers into your ears and making silly noises to see how funny your voice sounds.

duphlundling—babies' first finger paintings, usually drawn without paint on walls next to the cot.

Ee

eb—the mark made in the sand by a bottom, i.e. a bumprint.

eepnid—the sound made when a beetle is squashed underfoot.

effle—the space between the doors of the cubicle where you go to try on clothes before you buy them. These doors rarely close properly and can cause serious injury. See **effle-bang**.

The word comes from the name of a French engineer, Claude Effle, who was famous for making things that failed to work properly, such as the string coathanger and the underwater sandwich. The best known of these is the hotel he built where nothing fitted properly and the building was unable to be finished. Fortunately, the skeleton has become one of France's most popular tourist attractions—the Effle Tower.

Old use also as in describing something that has gone terribly wrong, e.g. "What an effle mess!" or "How effle!" Modern use has changed the spelling.

effle-bang—a bruise, usually on the head, that you get when you have your face up close to the effle (checking whether people can see you with your clothes off) and somebody tries to come into the booth. The effle-bang can also affect the knees, top of the head or the bottom. See **effle**.

egglet—the hole made in the wall of a toilet cubicle by the coat hook on the back of the door.

emgluk—the droopy stuff that hangs from the plug hole, but which won't wash down, no matter how much you prod or try to shift it with running water.

enswot—the yellow stain in the sink caused by a dripping tap.

ephlumpy—the skin that forms on the top of a hot milk drink or a bowl of custard.

essbender—someone who always sees the bad side of everything. See **sbendish**.

Ff

farbethink—any of those sayings parents use when they know they're losing a rational argument with their children, e.g. "Do as I say, not as I do," or "This hurts me much more than it hurts you," or, the worst of them, "When you grow up you'll not only understand this, you'll actually thank me."

fittlonger—someone who is forever finishing sentences for other people before they get the chance to say what they had in mind.

flakrip—the whiplash neck injury that comes from a severe sneeze.

flimpy—a kiss from someone with crinkly lips.

flummer—the sticky mess across the face when a bubble gum bubble bursts.

foonball—a perfectly formed spitball that clings together until it lands where it was aimed.

fotrimk—a belly button so flat and level with the rest of the tummy that it looks like the owner might be an alien.

frimble—a very cold toilet seat.

fripp—the sound your hanky makes when you have a cold and you open it up after it has dried out a bit.

Fritrumpers—the silliest people alive. Best known for such treasures as the Fritrumper "knock-knock" joke which goes like this:

Fritrumper: Want to hear a "knock-knock" joke?

Normal person: Yeah, sure.

Fritrumper: OK. You start.

They are also famous for the Fritrumping Festival at which thousands of Fritrumpers gather every year to display their latest inventions. Last year's prize winner was a solar-powered torch. Runner-up was the disposable oil tanker.

Fritrumpers are supposedly planning a space flight to the sun. When a "normal" pointed out that the sun would be very hot and that all the astronauts could be burned alive, the "Fritrumperonaut" explained that they had already thought of that problem. "That's why we are planning to go at night," he said smugly.

frokky—the moment when someone very important is caught in an embarrassing position in public, e.g. when a policeman is spotted using his glove instead of a hanky but is trying to make it look like he was really directing traffic.

frozz—the hairs that older people have growing in their ears.

Gg

gammoon—the ring left around a bath after someone has washed for the first time in a month.

gifdurgler—someone who sings in the toilet.

gimble—the tickling sensation in the nose just before a sneeze.

glapering—the empty look that creeps into someone's eyes when the person they are talking to has something hanging from their nose or trapped in their whiskers, making what they are saying very difficult to listen to. The listener's face "freezes" in faked concentration, as if they were actually listening very closely. The truth is they have not heard a word.

gnard—the small but painful cut you can get from paper.

gopp—a piece of food that is too chewy to break up, too big to swallow and too yucky to keep in your mouth. Also **gopp-box**—a small container to be used in an emergency, usually carried by old people in case they forget their false teeth. Also **gopp-fest**—the international festival for **gopping**, or disposing of a gopp without being noticed. Last year's Golden Gopp Award went to a retired magician, Mrs Gwen E. Ware, who successfully gopped three cows' hoofs and a fish hook into the judge's top hat without being seen.

gormy—any part of the pool where the water suddenly gets warmer, usually only for a very short time, sometimes with a change in colour.

grilfin—a mole with big hairs coming from it.

grimming—putting on a smile or "brave face" as disaster is just about to strike, e.g. when you shake hands with someone who thinks they have to break every one of your finger bones, but you can't let on it hurts because everyone is watching; or when you do the leap of the Masked Wonder on to your bike and the saddle is much harder than you thought but everyone is still watching.

grott-box—an old outdoor toilet, usually overgrown with vines but probably still in working order. Often inhabited by **underchompers**.

grundles—the rumblings in the abdomen (or lower) that give the false alarm that you are going to break wind.

guffocks—balls of hair from the moulting dog, found in corners, on plates, in ice-cream, on the openings of milk cartons, in your underwear drawer, and in the folds of the hanky you just used.

gurpen—the half of the worm that you see hanging from the apple you have just bitten into.

Hh

hellidrub—the runny stuff that has gone hard on the receiver of the public phone you have just tried to use.

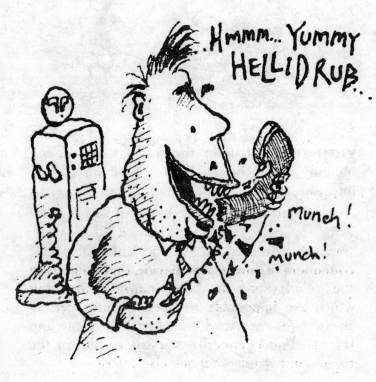

hoffgutting—making rude noises under your arms, often to pretend you are passing wind.

MoZART'S HoFFGuTTiNG CoNCERTo

hokespeken—the instructions on containers that tell you how to open them but which never work the way they are supposed to, e.g. the words that describe how to open the little plastic containers of jam or marmalade that come with the (cold) toast in hotel dining-rooms, but which are impossible to open without getting the spreads over your hands and the table and the chair and generally everywhere but on the toast ... unless it is someone else's toast.

horzenstinkenglimmer—the worst possible breath ever found on a human. It is said to be strong enough to be smelt up to twenty kilometres away if the wind is right. The condition is named after the Reverend Gordon Q. Shilbutt who was nicknamed "Horzenstinkenglimmer" for fun by his friends in the eighteenth century. Legend tells us that the Reverend became a hero one stormy night when ships were trapped offshore with no lighthouses to guide them. The Reverend Shilbutt was sitting on the wharf having his usual evening snack of gorgonzola cheese and toad's liver pâté. As he dined, the wind carried his breath out to the stranded ships. The captains had only to follow the scent to reach home safely. It is believed to be the origin of the phrase, "to follow your nose".

humb—the sudden surge in the head that comes from gobbling very cold ice-cream too quickly.

humphloss—the big balls of fluff that gather under the bed if you don't clean there often enough.

hyebotting—the peculiar walk of people as they enter the water at the beach or from the shallow end of the pool and try to keep the water from reaching the bottom of their swimsuits.

Ii

ib—a puddle, or splash, of unknown but suspicious origin on the toilet floor.

icklububbel—the sound made as the dog's food slides out of the can into the bowl.

idmukking—the way a dog (or cat) licks its own bum.

iffygirters—the marks on the leg of trousers when they have been used to clean their owner's shoes.

imfugling—the nervous and uncontrollable twitch that videogame players develop when that is all they do with their spare time. Victims are easily recognised by their bruises. These come not from playing the game, but because people they pass in the street mistake their imfugling for rude finger gestures.

inkment—the stain on a baby's clothing when its nappy is long overdue for changing.

ipkote—the sort of tan people get by wearing singlets or open-weave sandals in the sun. The effect is to make the person look as if they are still wearing the singlet or sandals.

Jj

jammy—any food that has been sat on.

jattering—the sound a dentist's drill makes in your head just before it is switched on.

jeelines—the stringy bits that can be peeled off a banana's flesh and wrapped around the handle of a little sister's breakfast spoon. They can also be placed carefully on a bowl of milk to make it look as if the cow had worms.

jimkin—a nip from sitting on a cracked toilet seat.

jipp—anything hanging from the nostril, mouth or whiskers that is not meant to be there.

joos—the watering in the eyes when a sneeze doesn't erupt properly.

jorble—the dribble that forms in the corner of the mouth as some people talk.

jumjum—any stain that is too embarrassing to talk about and which you try to hide. See **anti-jumjum**.

jurbling—the way sheets of toilet paper in some public toilets can be so jammed together that it is impossible to take out one sheet without pulling out twenty-five.

Kk

kairfull—an airborne and yet-to-land glob of bird-doo.

keegerfloot—any piece of food that flies through the air, e.g. during a pie fight; when someone becomes very excited while eating; or carried by the eater's mewkle. See **mewkle**.

klave—a deepset type of belly button, often difficult to keep clean.

kornflayks—pieces of skin scraped or picked off the hard, horny parts of feet.

kroklinger—the space between two relay runners that is just a bit longer than the baton neither of them has hold of.

kruelering—changes in the colour of the water in the pool when one of the swimmers does something they shouldn't have.

kruf—a detached scab.

kruf dinkling—a game played with krufs.

krundflugg—the scum that settles on the surface of water near drain outfall pipes or swimming pools which have not been serviced properly.

Ll

labbit—the drop that hangs from the end of your nose on a very cold day.

lawflug—dog's breath, not restricted to dogs.

leepy—any hair that grows entirely on its own in a prominent place, e.g. from the end of the nose or between the eyebrows.

limpwikkle—spots in a lawn where a dog has widdled and where the grass has changed colour.

lookwid—the oozy stuff from a pimple or under a blister.

lozwidge—a roll of toilet paper that doesn't have any perforations between the sheets.

lubber—the overhang of a pot-belly, i.e. the part that hangs over the trousers, looking like a sheet of tripe or a very thick, floppy pancake.

lumfray—the small bits of fluff that gather in the navel, no matter how often you clean it out.

cooperative lumfray Removal

Mm

mamber—the funny feeling when you have been crying and you try to chew something.

mawfinkry—describes the atmosphere in a changing room after a football game played in tropical conditions by players wearing full uniform.

mewkle—the spray that comes from some people's mouths as they speak. It is named after a certain teacher, Hortense Mewkle, who had the condition so badly that students sitting in the front seats of her classes carried their own umbrellas. There is one story, possibly an exaggeration, that Ms Mewkle once developed a severe cold that increased her complaint to the point where some students left school in small boats.

(Note: this book takes the idea of truth too seriously to endorse this story without access to solid—or even liquid—evidence.)

mibbling—the practice of filling in all the spaces in the letters on a page of print, e.g. mibbling.

mipps—the first hairs to appear under your arm, or other places where you never had hair before.

mobblefrod—a slave, the lowest of the low, employed by bullies to perform the lowest of the low tasks. Mobblefrods have been used to warm toilet seats on school camps, clean shower recesses with toothbrushes and count blades of grass on a cricket ground. "Frod" for short.

mongripper—a sandwich, cake or piece of fruit that has become the beginnings of a new ecosystem; usually the result of being left in a drawer or under books in a desk. It is most often the uneaten lunch from the last day of school, which was left in the humid conditions of the schoolbag over the Christmas holidays, and which now has a small population of things with lots of little legs.

moonbits—the white marks at the bottom of your fingernails.

mugraysh—landing face down in the mud during a sports match.

muldunkry—language learned by dentists so they can understand what their patients are saying when their mouths are full of cottonwool.

mulp—the sound made by something squishy hitting something hard, e.g. a mud pie or snowball hitting the back of a Fritrumper's head. Common use is "I mulped him!" Also, when an ice-cream falls from its cone to the ground—"Aw, mulped it. Can I have another?"

muphy—a small moustache on a woman's upper lip.

Nn

napwoddies—grown-ups who come to the beach without their bathers and who wander about in the shallows with their shoes and socks off and their trousers rolled up or their skirts tucked into their knickers.

nasgwurmer—someone who is easily disgusted and who has felt disgusted so many times that they have a permanent expression on their faces as though there is always a bad smell under their noses. It might be unfair to say it, but many nasgwurmers have been employed as librarians in very old buildings, as parking officers, and as information attendants in those little booths where they invite you to ask for help but would really rather you left them in peace.

nimbuckle—the marks left on the side of a drink glass by somebody else's lips.

noople—the piece of clothing that pokes through a person's fly when they forget to do it up. As in, "I see your noople," or "Guess who's wearing a blue noople today?" Or, to be cruel, "Noople alert!"

norb—someone who spends their break time in the loo with a bunch of magazines, usually recognised by the long desparate queue outside.

nottoon—someone who insists on whistling, even though nothing they whistle sounds like any tune ever composed. Nottoons have a short lifespan.

Nudwark—battle cry of the club for scaredy-cats. They meet regularly and take small steps towards becoming braver. For instance, one of their regular dangerous sports is the well-known "Budgie jumping" which involves Nudwark club members jumping over caged budgies without any safety nets, supported only by a thick rope tied around their ankles. As they perform their wimp-defying acts, they cry, "Nudwark!"

nug—something that a nosepicker left behind which has gone hard and stuck to the door handle, and which you have just discovered as you closed the door.

numbling—the sound of a tummy rumbling in an otherwise silent place, usually causing the tummy owner a lot of embarrassment, e.g. in the public library, in the theatre just after the hero and heroine have died tragically, or as everyone bows their heads and waits for someone to say grace.

nurbkumber—food that produces lots of strong burps, e.g. potato cakes and honey; lemonade and blue cheese; hot curry sandwiches with peanut butter.

Oo

obby—the artwork created by birds on the roofs of cars parked under their roosting trees.

olbrog—a very bony bottom, the sort that belongs to people who ride bikes with very skinny and hard seats.

onty—a female relative who insists on patting the heads of all her nieces and nephews when she greets them. As in the **onty-tank**, a piece of protective headwear for children with more than one onty in the family; or **onty-social**, a club for gatherings of onties, something to be avoided at all costs.

oonf—the short, sudden intake of breath when a warm part of the body comes in contact with something cold, e.g. a bottom on a cold toilet seat, or when the water in the pool reaches the bottom of your bathers.

orflug—a used travel-sickness bag.

Pp

pandly—the wrinkling of the skin on the fingertips and toes when you have been in the bath for a long time.

phumbl—a bubble blown in the bath, but not with your mouth.

pimkrannies—the bits of fluff or dirt that gather between your toes.

plooney—the ring mark around a fat tummy that comes from wearing a tight belt.

podlings—a game played with the marbles made by rabbits, usually found at the entrance to their burrows. (They leave them here for their next game.)

ponkle—the space between the floor and the bottom of the toilet door in public toilets.

ponkling—the practice of surprising someone through the ponkle space.

prudds—people who were pulling faces when the wind actually did change.

punkips—the seeds from any plant that are ideal for spit fights.

Qq

quadflix—a harmless-looking loose thread that you can't resist pulling, but when you do the whole jumper or sofa falls apart.

queedies—bits of food still stuck to the knives and forks that have been put out on the table for the next meal.

quinkling—the bleaching of doggy-doo in the sun.

quofflud—a very flat bottom. (Note: very common among male Spanish dancers, whose style of dancing has them peeping over their shoulder all the time to make sure that their quofflud is still there.)

quoncko—the pattern made on the bathroom mirror by flicking the toothpaste from the brush with your thumb.

quupnet—the name for all those things made out of clay in art class and which always end up looking like an ashtray.

Rr

ratchpinkle—the coloured lips of a person who has a complete (72-piece) set of felt tips, and who always sucks them while using them.

reeplay—secondhand chewing gum.

ribblox—the things that always make it look as if you've been eating carrots when you have been sick.

rimples—the pruny look on fat people's skin.

roatwringer—the machine that creates false laughter during TV shows that are not funny enough to risk having a live audience.

ronging—the almost inaudible sound made by someone who is trying to piddle in the toilet booth next to you without being heard.

ruddin-tin-tin—the rattle of small, hard, lumpy pieces sometimes found in babies' nappies.

ruffdinkle—the necessary "dance" of jitters and pacing performed by someone who needs a toilet urgently.

rullub—the food, sauce or runny stuff that immediately gushes out of the other side of the sandwich or hamburger you have just bitten into.

runkles—the red marks left on your bare knees when you rest your elbows on them as you lean forward to read the graffiti on the toilet door.

Ss

sbendish—any scene that is too ugly to bear, or a view of something very unsightly. It also describes the way things can look when you are depressed, i.e. everything looks bad. The origin is thought to come from the view of the world as seen by the toilet cistern or the s-bend of its plumbing. See **essbender**.

schmonking—the snorting that comes from uncontrolled laughter and which can cause the schmonker to discharge things from their nostrils unintentionally. The worst case of schmonking was when Mr Augustus Winchpole broke into a fit of laughter during a spaghetti-eating competition. He was disqualified for depositing food he had already eaten on the plates of other competitors.

Sorry I'm a little late today class... get on with your work...

scoring a stewpy—seeing someone important suddenly not looking so important, such as a teacher in their pyjamas, or cleaning their teeth, even wearing their slippers and dressing-gown during school camp.

shizz—long hair growing in the nostrils.

showdow—the silhouette on show from inside a canvas tent at night, or the show from inside the canvas "room" used as an outdoor toilet on camp—usually visible because the person using the toilet has taken their torch inside and left it on.

skug—something stepped in and which will not come off a shoe easily. Many skugs also have bad smells.

skwig—an insect that tries to enter a car through the windscreen while it is being driven at 100 km/h. No skwigs have ever been known to succeed.

snellow—yellow snow.

snogglum—when two lovers kiss so hard they create a vacuum and become stuck together.

souflay—soft, muffled sound made in a sleeping bag before its occupant gets up.

spibble—the midnight dribble that appears on the pillow.

splikkits—the marks left in your ice-cream cone by your dog's tongue.

spokkles—small scars caused by fiddling with scabs.

sponngle—to give someone a sharp blow to the head. Or to have been given a sharp blow to the head, e.g. "Not fair—I was sponngled!"

sponngles—the "stars" that appear before your eyes when you have had a knock on the head.

strool—the stringy dribble that hangs from a dog's chops.

strypes—the marks left on clothing or the back of the hand when a nose has been wiped without a handkerchief.

swigdee—a curly belly button that sticks out, sometimes enough to look like an extra button on a shirt.

Tt

tatlikkey—the flaky stuff that appears on your ears between showers that are too far apart.

tayres—the large pieces of dead skin that peel off after severe sunburn.

technipooper—the many different colours found inside babies' nappies.

teezing—the song of bloodthirsty revenge made at midnight by the only mosquito you didn't kill before you went to bed.

thignorf—a sloppy wet kiss from an old relative.

thucknob—a blocked nostril that usually comes with a heavy cold. Sometimes inexperienced nosepickers can become overly enthusiastic, resulting in a thucknob from a jammed finger. The suggested cure is to make them sneeze.

thucknobbing—holding one's nose to go under water, or because someone nearby has produced a strong souflay that has escaped from their sleeping bag. See **souflay**.

tidbobbing—trying to touch the end of your nose with the tip of your tongue.

toodle—the piece of shoelace that comes away in your hand when you try to tie it up and you're in a hurry and you haven't any spares and everyone is shouting at you to get a move on and you can't and it's not your fault, anyway, but the stupid shoelace maker's fault.

torbkinker—the haircut you didn't ask for, often created when the hairdresser tried to please both you and your parents by giving you a haircut somewhere between what you both wanted.

twillow—a pencil which has been sharpened so often that it is only just big enough to fit between the fingers.

Uu

ubber—the stretchy stuff in chewing gum that lets users pull long, sticky, stringy bits from their mouths. Plastic bread bags left too close to the toaster also contain ubber.

ucklushing—the patterns in the spittle in the sink when you clean your teeth. Some fortune tellers claim to be able to see a person's future by these patterns.

uddleb—the ring left on the skin by a plaster when it has been removed.

uffy—a toilet seat which is still warm from the previous user. In some very cold countries, whole families will organise their visits so that they take advantage of the uffy-effect (warmth) left behind by the person before them.

umble—anything that belongs in a hanky but which has rubbed off on to something else, e.g. the inside of your trouser pocket or the handle of your fork. The worst umbles are those found stuck between the pages of the book you have just borrowed from the library.

underchompers—small creatures that live in abandoned old buildings; also often in grott-boxes. They attack bare, sensitive fleshy parts of grott-box users. See **grott-box**.

uttboafing—the way voices sound when you are lying in the bath with your ears under the water.

Vv

vaplopping—eating fruity yoghurt with your spoon upside down so that you get the runny stuff without the lumpy bits.

veeps—the almost invisible fingernails of a compulsive fingernail chewer. These nails have been chewed back so far and are so small that the fingers look like small frankfurters.

chew my nails...
.. no way!!

vertwikkle—any shape accidentally made during a game of shadows on the bedroom wall which looks like the "naughty" bits of a human body.

vinjthib—the stringy spit that comes after eating ice-cream.

vronging—the little noises people make to let everyone else in the public toilet know that they are in this cubicle and no one can come in, even though there is no lock on the door and the sign doesn't work, so it still reads "vacant".

vutts—the spaces in between the keys on a piano, which eventually fill with crumbs from cakes eaten during practice, mixed with sweat and gucky stuff that rubs off the fingers. Filled vutts create new musical compositions by sticking the neighbouring keys so firmly together that it becomes impossible to play one key without also playing the one next to it.

Ww

waplish—sitting on a toilet seat that has just been washed.

warf—the heat generated by souflays. See **souflay**.

warpling—the peculiar walk of a baby with a full nappy.

weebies—the feelings experienced when bushwalkers realise the swamp they are halfway across (and up to their tummies in) is full of the biggest, sloppiest leeches ever seen.

wipple—the slight movement of the curtains caused by a burp or other form of air movement created by people or their pets (bulldogs are a common source of indoor wipples).

woff—the smell of a wet dog.

wongnuffy—any act that it is OK to do in private but which you have been caught doing in public, such as smelling your armpits when you thought the lift doors had closed, or scratching your bottom when you thought there was no one behind you. Also **wongnuffed**—being caught in the act of doing a wongnuffy.

woombling—the way rolls of flesh fold over each other on a fat body.

wuffies—pieces of peeled skin (usually from sunburn) rolled up into a ball for disposal.

Xx

xapwidlunkpymuffwegn—an ancient cure for hiccups. Saying this word frontwards and backwards one million times is guaranteed to cure the hiccups.

xodretching (say, *zodreching*)—using your legs (often at full stretch) to keep the toilet door (that has no lock) closed.

xtrappee—any widdling done somewhere that is not designed for the purpose, e.g. on the tree in the back garden when you have been locked out, in the fire bucket (full of sand) in the school hallway when the cleaner has locked the toilet doors, or in a fountain in the city when you just can't help it.

xtrumkin (say, *strumkin*)—the wonderful, sweet feeling of revenge that you know you shouldn't feel but you just can't help feeling as the person who snatched the last chocolate crackle (their seventeenth) at your birthday party rushes to the toilet with a green look on their face and a bulge in their cheek.

xuggleegow—the moaning song sung by the shopping trolley your parents have asked you to push and which has one wheel that will not turn round at all. Instead, it makes a noise like a ghost up a chimney, leaves a black trail on the vinyl floor and seems determined to turn every corner before you get to it.

Yy

yattfunkling—jumping up and down on one leg with your head cocked to the side as you try to get the water out of your ears.

yawb—the ugly cloud formation of flies around something that was not meant for them, such as your cream doughnut, the baby's sagging nappy or something the dog seems to like.

yiklob—the sound made when a person is gargling and the gargly stuff runs up the back of their throat and into their nose.

yingally—sitting on the cold porcelain of the toilet because you forgot to put the seat down. Also can mean sitting and forgetting to raise the lid, so that you sit on a flat surface.

yonk—the sound of heavy kissers coming apart.

yumpzog—any message or story where the most important bit has been lost, removed or not recorded, e.g. reading a mystery novel and discovering at the last moment that the final page is missing; listening to your answering machine go buzzy just as someone is leaving a message to tell you where to go to collect the prize in the raffle you entered; trying to use a public telephone and finding the page you need has been used to wipe something messy off the receiver. As in, "Oh, no! I've been yumpzogged!"

yungrotting—marks left on the shoulders of clothing by babies who burp up more than just wind when they are being "burped" after feeding.

Zz

zeepenbotters—the bits of food that can still be seen resting between the teeth, even though it is well past the time when the person should have cleaned them. Most zeepenbotters are a pasty yellow or white and are lodged in the places where the teeth meet the gums. It is very hard to talk to people with zeepenbotters and not stare at them. One trick, if a conversation must be had with a zeepenbotteree, is to look only at the end of his or her nose. This usually works, although it can lead to a lot of nervous and unnecessary nose-wiping. But what choice is there?

ziggy—the act of getting some part of the body caught or nipped in a zip.

zinnies—the squishy muck on your skin when you get lucky and actually manage to squash that mossie in your hands.

zok—the sound you hear when you pull your finger out of your ear.

zubgofen—the horrible feeling in the back of the throat when you have a heavy cold and you have just sniffed strongly, and you realise that it would have been less embarrassing and much neater if you have blown your nose.

zump—the sound (imagined) your heart makes when you realise you are in deep trouble, e.g. when you return home from the zoo and someone asks you where your little sister is; or when you ambush the biggest, meanest kid in the neighbourhood instead of your friends who went home a different way that day for the first time ever in their lives.